Kem,

Merry

Love,

Suzanne

For my beloved parents

WHO GAVE ME EVERYTHING

money cannot buy

The Christmas That Changed Everything

by Karen J. Ashton

illustrated by Elspeth C. Young

A true story

Snow is softly falling on the cabin.
Stars are twinkling over the mountain.
It has been a perfect Christmas day!

1

All the presents have been opened.
All the carols have been sung.
All the Christmas feast is cleared away.
All the lights are dimmed and the embers
of the yule log crackle and flicker in the darkness.
All the grownups are sitting around the table retelling old stories,
laughing, and eating another piece of pie.

All the little cousins lie fast asleep across
endless beds, bunks, sofas, and cribs.

All, that is, except for Molly Jo
who cannot go to sleep.

"Molly Jo," whispered Grammie.
"Let me tell you a story of a Christmas long, long ago."
"I think it will help you sleep."

3

Me

My Family

When I was just your age, my family and I lived in
a teeny tiny house that looked just like this to me . . .

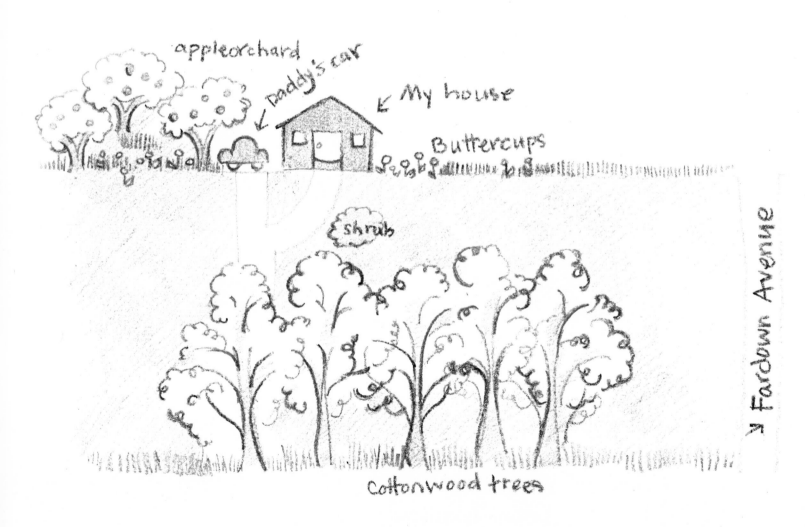

appleorchard

Daddy's car

My house

Buttercups

shrub

Fardown Avenue

cottonwood trees

My daddy was a telephone repairman. In terrible blizzards of snow, sleet, and driving rain, he would climb up telephone poles to fix the wires so others could call the doctor or an ambulance.

It was terribly dangerous! He was my hero.

My mommy was the general of the kitchen. She stirred big pots with her favorite wooden spoon and filled our tiny house with the most delicious smells. Daddy always said she made the best peasant food:
ham and bean soup,
hearty stews with home-
made bread, and cookies
hard and soft . . .

mostly hard.

I was the oldest and always
in charge . . .
at least most of the time.

Cora Lee was my little sister,
my pretended twin,
and my lookout when I was
doing something I shouldn't.

Little Kenny wasn't good for
much of anything yet.
Before he was born,
Daddy asked Cora Lee and me
if we would like a new
baby brother or a TV.

We said a TV.

We got Kenny anyway.

Butch → (our dog)

Our dog Butch only had one eye.
He had been in a fight with a cat
when he was a puppy
and lost his eye.

He hated cats!
So did I.

My neighborhood was a magical place. Fardown Avenue left the lighted streets of the city behind, crossed a small bridge, and then meandered slowly back and forth through tall cottonwood trees and old apple orchards that surrounded my little home.

There were pioneer houses, new houses, tree houses—and even some haunted houses. There were fields, irrigation ditches, secret paths, barns, dogs, horses, and lots of old parents to help the new ones.

Summer was splendid. Each hot day melted like butter into a delicious summer evening.

pioneer house
bridge
Barn
orchard
secret path
ditch

After dinner, children spilled out of their houses to play No Bears Are Out Tonight, Kick the Can, Red Rover Red Rover, and Hide and Seek until the mothers called their children home.

Summer was wonderful!

Fall was time for school,

Aa Bb Cc Dd Ee Ff Gg Hh Ii Jj

and Halloween.
I loved Halloween!

But winter was the BEST because of snow and Christmas.

Christmas

changed everything that came near it.

parkling Christmas trees
stood in the front window
of every home.

Wreaths hung on
all the doors.

Strands of
colored lights
framed each home
during the long
winter nights.

There was at least one snowman in front of every home—
and sometimes a whole family of them.

At night, from my window, I could see snowmen standing
guard over their dark and silent fields of snow.

If I opened our front door just a crack, I could smell the smoke
from all the neighborhood fireplaces on the evening air.

Even though it was bitterly cold outside,
I was sure it was warm and cozy inside every home.

At Oakwood Elementary School, my first-grade classroom
was filled with handmade decorations.

We made a gigantic paper chain—the longest ever made
in the history of man—and draped it around the whole room.

We made construction paper snowflakes and filled all the windows.
We wrote letters to Santa and covered the entire classroom door with
them, front and back.

Every day after lunch, my class gathered around the old black piano
and sang one of my favorite Christmas carols:

Jolly old Saint Nicholas
Lean your ear this way
Don't you tell a single soul
What I'm going to say
Christmas Eve is coming soon
Now you dear old man
Whisper what you'll bring to me
Tell me if you can

On the last day of school before Christmas,
we made cards for our parents, ate cupcakes,
and divided up the Christmas decorations.

Teacher said our parents would be
thrilled with the additional decorations.
I knew she was right. They were exquisite!

As my friends and I walked home that day, snow fell silently and all was still except for the occasional splashing of a passing car.

16

Our arms were full of decorations and cards,
while our thoughts were full of Christmas dreams and wishes.

Those wishes
bubbled up inside us
like the bubble lights on
my Christmas tree.

Tommy wanted a
new baseball and
mitt.

Linda wanted
a pair of skates.

Mikey wanted a big red
fire engine with a long
ladder and a new sled.

But there was only one
thing I wanted . . .
only one thing I
had asked for . . .
a Tiny Tears doll.

Tiny Tears came in beautiful pink box. She had thick, dark curly hair that you could wash. She was dressed in a small pink jacket and diaper. Her eyes closed slowly as you rocked her. She came with a bottle, and when you fed her, she cried real tears and wet her diaper!

She was just like
a real baby!
I wanted her
so very much.

19

"Merry Christmas!"
my friends and I shouted
to each other as we parted.

I could smell newly baked cookies
even before I got to my front door.

I dropped my Christmas load onto
the floor and rushed to the
kitchen to have a bite.

With a half-eaten cookie in
my hand, I called, "Mommy?"
But she didn't answer.

I quietly stepped into
my parents' bedroom.

There were snippets of
fabric all over the floor
next to Mommy's
sewing machine
and pieces of
wrapping paper
on the bed.

21

I knew I wasn't
supposed to be
in my mother's
bedroom—
especially this
close to
Christmas!

As I turned
to leave, I
saw something
on the floor
of the closet
that
stopped
my
breath.

22

It was a doll:
an old, dirty, beat-up, naked
Tiny Tears doll!

Somewhere deep inside of me,
I knew it was *my* Christmas doll.

I was horrified!

As I stared at that ugly doll,
my head filled with questions.

Why was I getting an old doll . . .
a doll with dirt in her hair . . .
a used doll . . .
a doll with no pink box or bottle . . .
a doll with missing eyelashes, scuffed-up cheeks,
and no clothes—not even a diaper!

I was stunned.

We must be poor!
I didn't know we were poor!

As these thoughts raced through my head, I heard our old car
pull up the gravel drive. I stepped out of the bedroom
into the kitchen and forced a smile onto my face.

As my family came through the back door,
Daddy laughed, "Well, tomorrow is Christmas Eve. Are you excited?"

I wasn't.

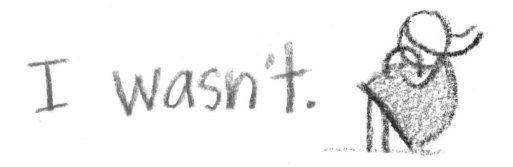

"We're going to spend all day tomorrow wrapping presents
and baking more cookies," said Mommy.
"It will be the best Christmas ever!"

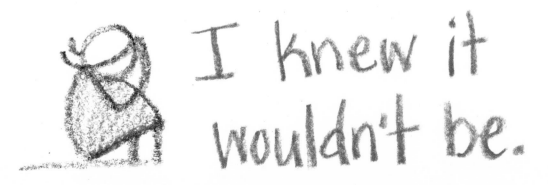

I knew it wouldn't be.

How could Mommy and Daddy be so happy when we were <u>so</u> poor!?

Now that I thought about it,
we had the smallest house in the neighborhood.

We had the oldest car,

our clothes were always
hand-me-downs,

and our dog had only one eye!

As I lay in bed that night,
tears silently trickled onto my pillow.
All my Christmas wishes would *not* come true.

That ugly, dirty doll haunted my dreams.

The very next day was Christmas Eve.
Mommy made raisin-filled Christmas cookies—my favorite!

They completely covered our little kitchen table.
Daddy laughed and said, "There is not so much as an inch left to eat on!"
We all laughed, but just then into my mind came the image of that
doll and I couldn't laugh anymore.

Raisin-filled Christmas Cookies (Karen's favorite)

(filling):
2 c. raisins
1/4 — 1/2 tsp. cinnamon
1 tsp. vanilla
2 tbl. butter
" " flour
1/4 cup water
1/2 " sugar

Put raisins, vanilla, & cinn. in a pan & cover w/ water. Boil 5 min. In a separate pan melt butter & stir in flour until well blended, then stir in water & sugar. Cook on low 2-3 min. until thickened, stir in raisins & cook for 1 min more. Set aside to cool while making cookie dough.

(Cookie Dough):
Combine butter, van. sugar, and sugar. Add in egg. Stir flour, salt, and bak. powder tog. in another bowl. Add dry mixture to butter mixture & add milk. Stir in well. Chill dough 30 min.

I forgot!
1 c. sugar

3/4 c. soft butter
2 packets vanilla sugar OR 1 tsp. vanilla
1 egg, beaten
3 cup flour
1 tsp. baking powder
pinch salt
1/2 c. milk

Roll dough 1/8 in. thick. Cut into 2 3/4 in. circles w/ round cookie cutter, place a cookie dough circle on covered baking sheet, place tbl. of filling in center of round, top w/ 2nd dough round & seal edges w/ fork.

Bake 375° for 10 min. or until lightly golden. (Makes abt. 4 dozen unless my back is turned...)

(side)

Daddy and I went outside and built the tallest snowman in the universe.

We even needed a ladder to put his hat on!

Mommy brought out mugs of hot chocolate.
We stirred them with a candy cane, then we ate the candy cane!

When the Christmas Eve stars began to twinkle,
we stomped the snow off our boots
and sang our way into the house.

Jolly old Saint Nicholas
Lean your ear this way
Don't you tell a single soul
What I'm going to say.

Daddy's voice shouted over the
top of everyone else,

"Christmas Eve is
HERE RIGHT NOW!"

Now, you dear old man
Whisper what you'll bring to me
Tell me if you can

I stopped.

I knew that "dear old man" would *not*
be bringing me what I had wished for.

In my mind, I saw the doll on the floor of the closet again.
I shook my head to get rid of the picture.

The lights from our tree filled our little living room with a soft glow. We didn't have a fireplace where we could hang our stockings, but Daddy said it didn't matter and that we should each choose one of his longest work stockings and place it under the tree.

So, we did.

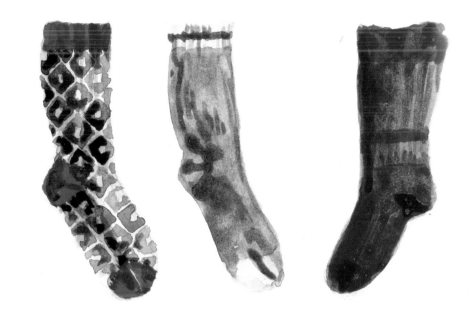

As Daddy tucked me in that night, he said, "I hope you have the best Christmas ever."

As I lay in bed, I knew something had changed.
The old idea of what Christmas *should* be
was broken inside of me.

There was an aching in my chest. An idea both beautiful
and important was growing inside of me, pushing its way into my
heart and mind. It was so much bigger than a doll. It was about
Daddy, Mommy, Cora Lee and Kenny, our little house, and
everything warm and happy inside.

I knew Daddy and Mommy wanted to give me
the doll in the pretty pink box, but they couldn't.
I knew that made them sad. I never wanted them to be sad!

The ache in my heart was
now in my throat.
I loved my parents!
I wanted *them* to have
the best Christmas ever,
but I had nothing
to wrap and put
under the tree.

I made a plan.

I would be brave. I would be grateful.
I would be happy for whatever was under the Christmas tree.
NO MATTER WHAT!

The next morning,
I awoke to the sound of Daddy's voice.

"RISE AND SHINE, IT'S CHRISTMAS TIME!"
he bellowed.

I slid over the side
of the top bunk and
landed momentarily
on Cora Lee.
Daddy picked
Kenny out of his
crib and steadied him
on the floor.

"Let's go see what's under the tree," Daddy chuckled.
Cora Lee and Kenny squealed as they ran into the living room.

I steeled myself against
the disappointment I
knew was coming.
I took a deep
breath and
filled my
lungs
with
all the
courage
and love
that I had.

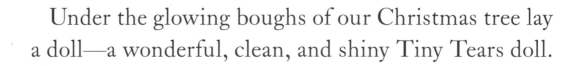

Under the glowing boughs of our Christmas tree lay
a doll—a wonderful, clean, and shiny Tiny Tears doll.

She was wearing a beautiful white, lacy nightgown.

I knew it was the doll I had seen in the closet
because she was still missing her eyelashes,
but now her hair was clean and
curled around her little face.

Her cheeks were rosy again.

There was a little wooden bed painted pink, and in it
there were tiny dresses, overalls, shirts, jackets, and pants.
She even had a soft flannel quilt to keep her warm,
and a bottle . . . a bottle!

The breath I had been holding went right out of me.

I dropped to my knees and took her in my arms.
She was the most beautiful doll in the whole wide world!

Someone had lovingly worked magic.
She was better than the doll in the pink box.
She had clothes and a bed and a bottle and it was all just for me!
I looked up through my tears at Mommy and Daddy. They smiled back.
That beautiful ache was back again.

I wrapped the quilt around my new
baby doll, climbed up next to
my mommy, and snuggled
into her arms.

That
Christmas
changed everything.

As Grammie finished her story,
Molly Jo smiled and slipped into sleep.

Acknowledgements

Karen and Elspeth would like to extend special thanks to the following, without whose gracious help this project would not have been possible:

Alan Ashton

Al and Nancy Young

Jeff and Karen Acerson

Tanner M. Young

Eliza and Mary Ann Smith

Traci and Molly Jo Ashton

Hillary, Jack, and Sophie Maas

Frank Maas

Allison Ashton Norton

Adelaide Ashton

Brittan Young

Molly Goo

Holly Fairbanks at Oakwood Elementary

Lynda Hendrickson at UpperCase Printing, Ink.

Jim Ekenstam and staff at North Star Printing

Julie Duckett and staff at Perfect Register

Muffy "the Brave"

and Tiny Tears

Karen also wishes to express her deepest thanks to her daughter, Rebekah Ashton Westfall, whose expertise in children's literature has been invaluable during the writing of this book.

Edited by Karen L. Acerson
Designed by Tanner Young & Elspeth C. Young

Manufactured in the United States of America

Library of Congress Cataloging-in-Publication Data

Names : Ashton, Karen J. | Young, Elspeth, illustrator.
Title : The Christmas That Changed Everything / by Karen J. Ashton ; illustrated by Elspeth C. Young.
Description : Orem, Utah : Al Young Studios, 2019.
Summary : Karen remembers how the gift of a doll at Christmastime
changed her childhood understanding of the power of love and Christmas.

Printed in 2019
North Star Printing, 131 West 2050 North, Spanish Fork, Utah 84660-9512
10 9 8 7 6 5 4 3 2 1